PHILIPPOS MANDILARAS

The Twelve Gods of Olympus

Illustrations
Natalia Kapatsoulia

PAPADOPOULOS PUBLISHING

The Twelve Gods of Olympus

Text: Philippos Mandilaras
Illustrations: Natalia Kapatsoulia
Translation: Alison Falkonakis

PAPADOPOULOS PUBLISHING
www.epbooks.gr

9, Kapodistriou str., 14452 Metamorfossi Attikis
Tel.: +30 210-2816134
e-mail: info@epbooks.gr
Bookshop
14, Massalias str., 10680 Athens
tel.: +30 210-3615334

ISBN 978-960-569-564-4

There were twelve gods, each one extraordinary,
and they lived high up on beautiful Mount Olympus,
the tallest mountain in Greece.
They fought huge beings called Titans and Giants,
wild beasts and monsters, taking them captive and throwing them
deep into dungeons in the bowels of the earth.
These twelve became masters of the world,
ruling the land, the seas and the skies.

In the beginning there was nothing, just thick, dark
blackness. No night, no day, no sound.
Out of this blackness Mother Earth was born.
Her name was Gaia.

From Gaia all life was created: the land and
the mountains, the seas and the skies.
She created the trees and the plants to grow
on her land, and the sun and the stars to shine
in the heavens.

Gaia created a god called Uranus to rule the heavens, and he and Gaia joined together to create the children of the earth.

Titans

Hundred-handers

Cyclops

The first children were not human like you and me.
They were huge Titans, one-eyed Cyclops, Giants
and beasts called Hundred-handers.

As his children grew, Uranus became frightened
that they would take his throne from him.
He wanted to be sure that he would always
be the ruler, and so he took his children and closed
them away in the depths of the earth.

His youngest son, Cronus, was a huge Titan
who was very cunning and very strong.
Cronus discovered his father's wicked plan and he
asked his mother, Gaia, what he should do.
Gaia told him that he should fight his father
and take over as the ruler.

So Cronus fought his father and took his throne.
With their mother Gaia's blessing, Cronus
married a beautiful Titan girl named Rhea
and they became the new rulers of the earth and the skies.

Soon Cronus, like his father, became frightened
that his children would grow up and steal his
throne from him, and so when each child was born, he took
it and swallowed it whole, making himself fatter and fatter!

His wife Rhea played a trick on him. When their sixth baby
was born, she hid it safely in a cave, high on a mountainside
on the island of Crete. In place of the baby she gave her husband
a rock wrapped in a blanket to swallow.

That lucky baby was named Zeus and he grew up
without his family, high on a far off mountain,
with goat milk for food
and only the beautiful mountain nymphs to care for him.

As the years passed, Zeus grew big and strong. He learned what had happened to his brothers and sisters, and he decided that he had to find a way to save them.

Hestia

Demeter

Hera

Hades

Poseidon

Zeus used all of his strength to fight his father.
He won the battle and freed his brothers and
sisters from his father's stomach, back into
the daylight so that they could live.

First he took the rock which his mother had fed to his father,
then one after the other the others were saved.

Next Zeus freed the Cyclops and the Hundred-handers
from their prison deep in the earth.
They were very grateful to Zeus and they promised
that they would help him if he ever needed them.

Very soon Zeus needed their help, as a terrible war
began between the Gods and the Titans. The war was
called the "Battle of the Titans". On the one side were the huge Titans,
and on the other the six gods, the Cyclops and the Hundred-handers.

The gods of Olympus fought hard and won the battle. The Titans
were captured and put into dungeons deep in the earth.

Then the gods decided among themselves who would be
the god of the underworld, the land, the sea and the heavens.

Hades was given the underworld,

Poseidon, the seas,

Zeus, the sky and heavens.

They decided that they should all rule the land together,
with Zeus, who had rescued them, as their King and leader.

As the years passed, more and more gods were born.
Each one was beautiful, but more importantly
each one was worthy of their role.

Artemis: goddess of hunting

Zeus: leader of the gods and men

Hermes: messenger of the gods and god of trade

Aphrodite: goddess of love and beauty

Poseidon: god of the seas

Hera: wife of Zeus, queen of the world

Demeter: goddess of farming and agriculture

Hestia: goddess of the home

But the war of the gods was not quite over.
Gaia was very angry that the gods held her Titans prisoners
and so she encouraged the Giants to fight the gods.

For many years the gods fought the Giants.
Hercules and Dionysus, who were half human and half god,
also helped in the battles until, finally, the Giants lost
and peace was at last brought to the land.

From then on, the gods lived peacefully on Mount Olympus
and from the top of their mountain they ruled the world.
The ancient Greeks worshipped the twelve gods
and built them many beautiful statues and huge temples.